MICRO BATTLE ROBOTS

Build Your Own

Written by Lisa Regan
Illustrated by Hardlines

TOP THAT! Kids™

Published by Top That! Publishing plc
Tide Mill Way, Woodbridge, Suffolk IP12 1AP, UK
www.topthatpublishing.com
Copyright © 2004 Top That! Publishing plc
Top That! Kids is a Trademark of Top That! Publishing plc
Mini Maestro is a Registered Trademark of Top That! Publishing plc

Prepare for Battle!

You are about to become a robot master, able to build your own robots and send them into battle against each other!

At the same time, you will learn lots of interesting stuff about the world of science and invention, and practise some basic engineering and construction skills. This kit contains everything you need to build your own battle robots, including instructions for six different battle machines. Choose your favourite, find an opponent and prepare to do battle!

What is a Robot?

First of all, let's figure this out. A robot is a machine with moving parts that can be programmed to do a job without having human help.

Most robots do not look like humans.

Robot Functions

It can be as simple as your VCR when it's programmed to tape something without you being there. It can be as complicated as a machine sent into space to explore another planet.

Moving Parts

It's easy to imagine a robot like C-3PO from the *Star Wars* movies. He walks and talks like humans. However, many robots are fixed in one place and just have moving arms to do their work.

FACT!
A robot that looks like a human is called an android.

Science Fiction Stuff

In 1921, a Czechoslovakian writer called Karel Capek wrote a play called *R.U.R. (Rossum's Universal Robots)*. It was about machines which did all the work for people. The Czech word he used for the machines was 'robota' and the word was adapted into English.

Isaac Asimov

Twenty years later another sci-fi writer called Isaac Asimov wrote about robots. In his vivid imagination, he saw a world full of robotic machines doing human work.

He must have predicted very advanced robots, though, which might try to take over the world, because he also wrote about three robot laws.

Robot Laws:
1) Robots must never harm humans.
2) Robots must follow human instructions as long as they don't break rule 1.
3) Robots must protect themselves without breaking the other rules.

Real-life Robots

In the real world, machines have been used for hundreds of years, especially since the Industrial Revolution in the 1700s and 1800s.

Programming

However, it is only really since the development of computers in the mid-20th century that humans could properly programme machines to do chosen jobs.

Intelligent Robots

Even today, robots can't do some things as well as humans. They walk and run like toddlers and aren't anywhere near as clever as humans.

A bomb disposal robot.

Dangerous Jobs

Robots can be sent into dangerous places, like space, or war zones and can be used in factories to do jobs that are too boring for humans – they don't need lunch breaks or holidays either.

Movie Star Robots

The ideas we have about robots usually come from TV or the movies starring characters like these.

Terminator

Arnold Schwarzenegger plays an amazing type of cyborg, or machine, called a T-800. It looks and acts human, but is programmed to destroy humans on Earth. Unfortunately for the humans trying to escape it, the T-800 is indestructible.

Robocop

This movie has a part-robot, part-human as its main character!

A US policeman gets killed in action, but is rebuilt with robot parts to become a superhuman cop!

Commander Data

Data is an ideal member of the *Star Trek* crew, being able to command the starship *Enterprise* on the night shift, when humans need to sleep. He has a humanoid form and can learn to copy human behaviour.

Movie Star Robots

C-3PO

In *Star Wars* language, C-3PO is a 'droid' – a robot with human form and complex programming to perform particular jobs.

C-3PO is fitted with a communication module, allowing him to speak over six million galactic languages. Unfortunately, he also has personality modules, allowing emotions and feelings – and lots of moaning!

R2-D2

This cute little robot, also from *Star Wars*, shows, perfectly, how robots don't have to take human form. R2-D2 does not speak human languages, but communicates with beeps and whistles.

Robots in Space

Robots are vital in modern space exploration. They really do venture 'where no man has ever gone before...' just like the sci-fi stories say.

Missions to Mars

In 1975 the Viking mission dropped a robot onto the planet's surface. It provided us with important and amazing information, such as the temperature of the planet, which was shown to vary up to 50°C in one day.

Venturing to Venus

Ten years after this Viking mission, a different kind of robot was sent to Venus. It was an aerobot – a robot designed to float around a planet in the atmosphere. The aerobot was called the *Venus Vega*.

Viking 2 – the Mars lander.

Exploration Robots

It's difficult and dangerous for humans to explore some of Earth's harsher environments, so unmanned robots can be used for these projects.

Jason

Jason is a robot the size of a small car, and has been used to explore ancient shipwrecks which have settled deep on the ocean floor. It can dive down to 6,000 m (20,000 ft) – nearly deep enough to cover Mount Everest!

Roboshark

This robot was used to film amazing new TV footage of sharks. It's much safer than sending in a human diver to come face to face with dangerous creatures!

RoboLobster

Cool! This robot looks like a real lobster, and is sent to the sea bed to search for dangerous mines (explosives) which could destroy ships.

RoboLobster crawls underwater.

Robot Toys

Not all robots are used for serious tasks. Some of them have been invented just to keep you amused! Many toy companies now sell robotic toys and games.

Soccer Pro

This is a robot you can build yourself, and its main purpose is to play soccer! It can turn and move in any direction on the floor, accelerate past other players, and catch and shoot a ball. Watch out Ruud van Nistelrooy!

Transformers

Robots in disguise! These great characters started in the 1980s and have been re-released since then as new cartoons and characters. Each character has its own robotic form, but then can transform into something different, usually a super car or vehicle.

Transformers.

Robot Toys

AIBO.

AIBO

Invented by Sony, AIBO is an amazing robotic dog. The really clever thing about it is that it can learn new things. It has several programmes which make it behave like a living creature, and its behaviour will change as it responds to its owners.

Furbies

Probably the cutest robots in this book! Furbies have complex programming that allows them to move and interact in many ways – they dance to music, they learn new tricks when you praise them, and they talk to you when you feed them or play games together.

First brought out in 1998, the company that made them said the originals had more processing power than the first lunar module on the Moon!

Furbies talk to you when you play with them.

Robots in War

If robots can replace humans in space and deep underwater, they can also be used in other dangerous situations, such as the middle of a war zone.

AROD

This is an Airborne Remotely Operated Device – a flying robot. It was used in the 1980s to fly over target areas and send back images of danger zones via fibre optic cables. It was quite unstable in flight, so is no longer used.

AROD could provide short range aerial surveillance.

Robots in War

SARGE

Its name stands for Surveillance and Reconnaissance Ground Equipment. Its job is to be the first onto a battlefield, so that it can work out where the enemy is, what equipment the soldiers might need and what they will be faced with in battle.

MERV

This remote-controlled robot looks like it should be on a building site! It is actually a much-used bomb disposal vehicle. It can be used to blow up or disarm bombs without endangering soldiers.

SARGE.

How do Robots Work?

Robots are made up of different parts, some for 'thinking' or instructions, some for moving and working. The outer shell, or body, protects the delicate operating systems inside.

Energising

In order to carry out any operation, a robot needs energy, or power. Once energised, the robot can begin to think, carry out commands and perform its programmed manoeuvres.

Stamp boards tell robots what to do.

Brain Power

Robots don't have a brain like humans, but they can have the next best thing: a computer. Some robots have huge 'brain power' with large amounts of circuitry and memory to allow them to learn, and carry out, complex commands. Others have limited brain power, as they are only designed to perform a single, simple function.

How do Robots Work?

Movement

Robots on wheels can move in a limited way. Making a robot walk on legs is much more difficult for their designers. Similarly, giving a robot hands which work like human hands is hugely tricky. Picking up an egg without breaking it may seem easy to you, but it's one of the hardest things to programme a robot to do.

Battle Robots

Your Battle Bots are powered by a motor based on a coiled spring mechanism. When you pull it back the mechanism is tightened. When released, it drives your robot forward. On top of this mechanism is your robot body – your choice of outer shell, customised and fine-tuned for fighting!

Tiger Bot – ready for battle.

Turn the page to start assembling your battle robots from the kit!

15

Croc Bot

Choose this battle robot if you want a lean, mean fighting machine!

✓ **Strengths**: stable double wheel base; unique scoop can tip opponents off balance.

✗ **Weaknesses**: limited selection of weaponry.

Component parts:
body shell; chassis; base; bumper; scoop; smasher; 2 x target pieces; rear motor axle; front axle

CONSTRUCTION

1 Push out the body pieces you will need, and press out the pre-cut slits and tabs.

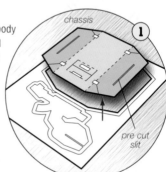

chassis

pre cut slit

Croc Bot

(2) Fold the chassis into shape, as shown. Slot the rear motor axle through the angled slots at the back of the chassis, and fix into place in the motor slots.

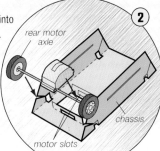

rear motor axle

chassis

motor slots

(3) Slot the front axle through the front slots and into place.

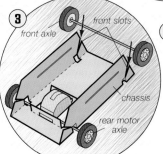

front axle

front slots

chassis

rear motor axle

4 Fold the base along the score lines and into shape. Fold down the ends of the tabs on each side of the base, where marked. Now slot the tabs through the sides of the chassis to hold the two parts together. When the side tabs are in the slots, move the ends up again to keep them in place.

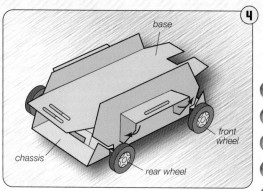

base

chassis

front wheel

rear wheel

NB *Make sure that the two prongs of the base are at the front of the chassis, and the two slots are at the rear.*

Croc Bot

5 Fold the main body shell into shape. Use the tabs at the sides and rear of the body shell to fix it to the base. Make sure the rear body tab fits into the inner slot on the base, leaving the outer slot for later.

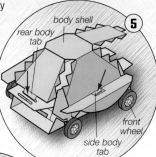

body shell

rear body tab

5

front wheel

side body tab

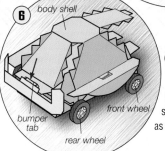

body shell

bumper tab

front wheel

rear wheel

6 Fold the bumper into shape and slot the tab into the outer slot on the base, as shown.

Croc Bot

7 Now for your Croc Bot's weaponry! To bash your opponents, fold the smasher along the scored lines and keep it in shape using the small tabs.

8 Attach the smasher to the front of the croc bot by slotting it onto the two front prongs. Keep it in place using the remaining tab at the front of the main body. Fit this securely into the slot on top of the smasher.

Croc Bot

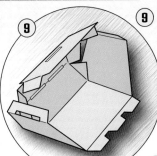

9

9 Or, fold the smasher into shape and slide the mouth tabs through to the inside of the shape. Secure this weapon in the same way as the smasher.

10 Fold the targets into shape and attach them to the Croc Bot on top of the main body shell, as shown.

Now turn to page 40 for the rules of combat. Watch out, Croc Bot is on your case!

Frog Bot

This robot is solid, reliable and catches opponents unaware!

✓ **Strengths**: sturdy bodywork with added bumper for protection.

✗ **Weaknesses**: easily dislodged weaponry.

CONSTRUCTION

Component parts:
body shell; chassis; base; bumper; spinning disk; flame thrower; 2 x target pieces; rear motor axle; front axle

1 Fold the chassis into shape following the score lines. Slot the rear motor axle, and the front axle into place, as shown.

2 Fold down the ends of the tabs on each side of the base. Now slot the tabs through the sides of chassis to secure the two pieces together.

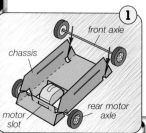

front axle
chassis
motor slot
rear motor axle

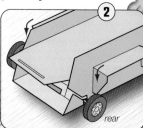

rear

Frog Bot

3 Fold the main body shell and slot its three tabs into the base. Two tabs slot into the two front slots, with a single larger tab at the rear.

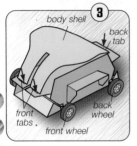

3

body shell

back tab

front tabs

back wheel

front wheel

4

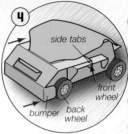

side tabs

front wheel

bumper   back wheel

4 Fold the bumper section into shape and fix it in place on the base section using the slots on the side tabs.

5

5 Choose your weaponry and attach your targets, as shown.

Now turn to page 40 for the rules of combat. Frog Bot's gonna getcha!

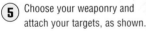

23

Tiger Bot

Don't let this king of the ring out of your sights!

✓ **Strengths**: height over opponents can be an advantage.

✗ **Weaknesses**: less stable body design and vulnerable weaponry.

Component parts: body shell; chassis; base; support bridge; chain saw; wrecking ball; 2 x target pieces; rear motor axle; front axle

CONSTRUCTION

1. Carefully score along the dotted lines on each piece. Press out the pre-cut slits and tabs.

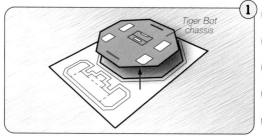

Tiger Bot chassis

1

Tiger Bot

(2) Fold up the central flaps on the chassis which will hold the axle in place.

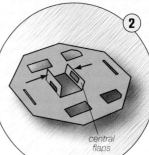

central flaps

front base tab

rear base tab

(3) Fold the base and push the front axle through the front slots and the rear axle through the rear slots. Attach to the chassis using the tabs at the front and the rear of the base.

Tiger Bot

(4) Fold down the nose on the support bridge. Slide the tabs on the bridge into the slots at the top of the base. Make sure the bridge slots down far enough for the legs to touch the chassis.

support bridge

4

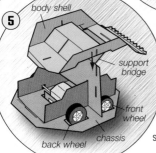

body shell

support bridge

front wheel

back wheel

chassis

(5) Fold the main body shell into shape. The sides of this part should be folded upwards. Slot the sides down onto the top slots of the support bridge.

Tiger Bot

6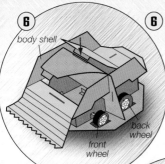

body shell

back wheel

front wheel

6 The remaining tab on the body shell (by the top tiger logo) slots into the support bridge.

7 There is one more tab on the support bridge, under the tiger's nose. Slot this into the body shell, just above the teeth.

support bridge

teeth

Tiger Bot

8 The weapon goes at the rear of the main body shell. Attach your chosen weapon by sliding the larger handle into the large slot of the main body shell. Keep it secure using the small part of the handle to slide into the smaller slot.

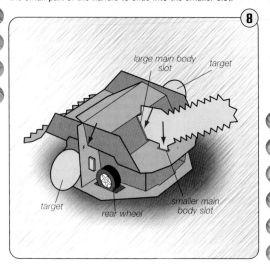

large main body slot

target

target

rear wheel

smaller main body slot

Tiger Bot

(9) Slide the targets into the remaining slots on the sides of the support bridge, as shown.

Now turn to page 40 for the rules of combat. The tiger is on the prowl again!

(9)

Crab Bot 🦀

Watch out for this circular nasty – it doesn't scuttle, it's a killer!

✅ **Strengths**: low centre of gravity gives stability; double power from spinning discs.

❌ **Weaknesses**: vulnerable targets.

Component parts: body shell; chassis; base; support bridge; claws; double spinning blades; 2 x target pieces; rear motor axle, front axle

CONSTRUCTION

1 Fold the base and push the front axle through the front slots and the rear axle through the rear slots.

NB *Crab Bot has two slots at its rear end, instead of just one.*

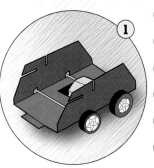

Crab Bot 🦀

(2) Fold up the central flaps on the chassis. Attach the base to the chassis using the tabs at the front and the rear of the base. Use the inner rear slot, leaving the outer rear slot free for later.

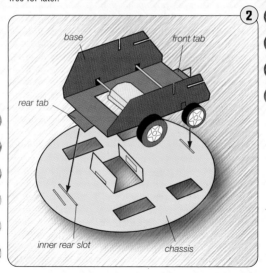

base

front tab

rear tab

inner rear slot

chassis

Crab Bot

3 Slot the support bridge onto the base, just behind the front wheels.

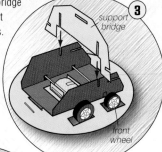

support bridge

front wheel

4 Fold the main body shell. Slot the rear main body tab into the outer slot at the rear of the chassis. Then attach it to the support bridge with the tab at the front of the body shell.

main body shell

Crab Bot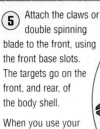

(5) Attach the claws or double spinning blade to the front, using the front base slots. The targets go on the front, and rear, of the body shell.

When you use your Crab Bot, you can insert the side slots on the main body shell into the slots on the support bridge if this helps your model to run more smoothly.

Now turn to page 40 for the rules of combat.

(5)

front base slots

claws

Bull Bot

For sheer strength and force, you can't go wrong with Bull Bot.

- **Strengths**: extra protection from shield.
- **Weaknesses**: unsteady because of single axle wheel base.

Component parts:
body shell; chassis; base; shield; blade; hammer; 2 x target pieces; rear motor axle

CONSTRUCTION

(1) Carefully score and fold along all the lines on the press-out parts. Fold the chassis into shape, press up the central flaps and put the rear motor axle in place.

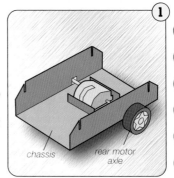

chassis

rear motor axle

Bull Bot

2

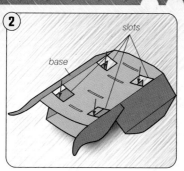

slots

base

2 Fold and shape the base section. Attach it to the chassis using the four tabs and slots. Make sure the horns are at the front and the motor at the rear.

3 Fold the main body shell into shape. Position this section over the base with the slots and tabs aligned with the slots on the base. Push through the two tabs. Make sure the bumper is on the rear.

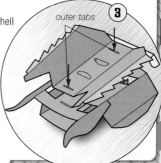

outer tabs

3

Bull Bot

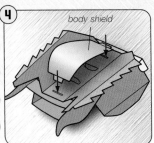

4 body shield

4 Link the body section to the body shield by inserting the tabs on the shield through the aligned slots on the shell and base underneath.

5 Use the slot at the back of the shield to attach your weaponry. Fit the targets at the sides of the body shell.

Now turn to page 40 for the rules of combat. Beware the charge of the bull!

Hammerhead Bot

It's not a fish out of water – it's a monster on the loose!

✅ **Strengths**: fast and low with lighter axle and bodywork.

❌ **Weaknesses**: limited weaponry and vulnerable targets.

Component parts:
body shell; chassis;
base; bumper; laser gun;
magnet; 2 x target pieces;
rear motor axle

CONSTRUCTION

1 Fold the chassis into shape, pressing up the central flaps, and secure the rear motor axle in place.

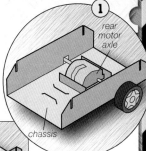

2 Fold the base section and secure to the two tabs.

Hammerhead Bot

3 Fold the main body into shape. Use the four tabs underneath the body shell to attach it to the chassis. Slot the remaining tab at the front of the body shell into the slot at the front of the base.

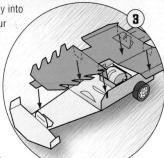

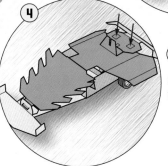

4 Fit the bumper using the two slots at the rear of the body shell.

Hammerhead Bot

5

5 Choose your weapon and attach it to the top of the body shell at the rear. It slots between the body shell itself and the bumper.

6 Don't forget to fit the targets into the remaining slots.

Now turn to page 40 for the rules of combat. Hammerhead's here and he wants to fight!

Rules of Combat

Although all is fair in robot battles, you still need to set out some ground rules to ensure nobody heads home in a sulk.

Scoring System

- Set up a points scoring system. Score at the end of each round (see the rules opposite for organising the rounds).

- Award one point for any target that is knocked off balance.

- Award two points for a target that is completely dislodged from its robot.

- Destroyed weapons (that is, those that are knocked away from the robot) score three points.

- Damage to bodywork, other than targets and weaponry, scores a whopping five points.

- Removal from play (by tipping) scores a maximum ten points.

Rules of Combat

Damage Repairs

- Before you start, decide how many times per round you are allowed to recharge your motor and make new attacks on your opponent. Alternatively, play against the clock. A minute for each round is a good amount of time to bombard your enemy and make them pay the price of challenging you.

- After each round, remove your robot from the battle zone. You must agree on the repairs that are allowed at this stage.

Your aim is to reduce the number of points easily available to your opponent – partly destroyed body parts will be the first point of attack for them when you resume battle.

- You could decide to compete without targets and the battle until one of you is destroyed.

Let Battle Begin

Select and build your robot of choice, and find an opponent with a robot that's ready to fight.

- You should mark out a battle zone to help you judge the fight fairly. Play on a firm, smooth surface to get the best out of your Battle Bot.

- Erect a perimeter fence using the spines of heavy books.

- Limit your battle zone to no more than one metre square to get the best performance from your Battle Bots.

- Toss a coin to see who chooses their end of the arena. Take your place behind your robot and position it inside perimeter fence.

Let Battle Begin

- Press firmly on the axle, taking care not to dislodge your own weaponry or targets, and pull back your robot to charge up the motor.

- On the count of three, release it. Make sure your aim is true to get a direct hit on your opponent!

Bot Shop

- Some adjustment may be necessary to make your models run smoothly. Make sure nobody sections obstruct the wheels.

- If you are using the targets, make sure they are positioned fairly loosely on the models.

- Create spare sections in case anything tears, by tracing around each body section onto thin card.

DO NOT SCRATCH THE BEST FURNITURE IN THE HOUSE OR THE WAR WILL BE BETWEEN YOU AND YOUR PARENTS!

Battle Robot Tournaments

If you have several robot builders who wish to fight, you can stage a tournament. Remember – the more fights you enter, the weaker your robot may become.

Knockout Tournament

- Each entrant should have one robot. Write the robot names on scraps of paper and fold each scrap in half. Shuffle the papers in a jar, and draw out one at a time.

- Use the table on pages 46–47 to record the contestants and their chosen robot. The first drawn does battle against the second, the third fights the fourth, and so on.

Battle Robot Tournaments

- If your tournament is a straight knockout competition, the winner of each of the battles goes through to the next round. The table overleaf uses all six robots from this kit, so the fourth semi-final place goes to the highest-scoring loser.

League Championship

- If you prefer to stage a league-based tournament, use the alternative table. Record two or three entrants in each mini-league. Each does battle against the other members of their group, one by one, and records their score.

- Add up the total battle scores of each robot. The winner from league 1 goes into the grand final against the winner from league 2.

Knockout Tournament

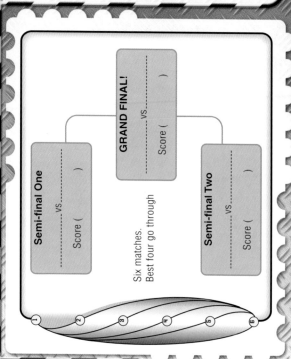

GRAND FINAL!

---------- vs ----------

Score ( )

Semi-final One

---------- vs ----------

Score ( )

Semi-final Two

---------- vs ----------

Score ( )

Six matches.
Best four go through

League Championship

TOURNAMENT CHAMPION:

League Tables

League One

Robot name:	Match scores:		Total score:
	(1)	(2)	
1			
2			
3			

Group winner:

League Two

Robot name:	Match scores:		Total score:
	(1)	(2)	
1			
2			
3			

Group winner:

GRAND FINAL!

----------------vs----------------

Score (   )

TOURNAMENT CHAMPION:

Multi-player Battles

If you don't want to organise a tournament, but have four or six players, you can play 'Tag Battle Bots'!

- Divide into two even teams. Think of a fun team name for each if you like.

- Nominate one robot per team to enter the battle zone first. Start to fight using the normal rules. However, if your team's robot is getting weakened more quickly, you can 'tag' another team member.

- To tag your team mate, you must recharge your motor and return to the perimeter of the battle zone.

- Your robot now leaves the battle zone and your team mate takes up the fight.

GOOD LUCK!